W9-AXP-984

CLEAN SCHOOL BUS USA

Sponsored by the U.S. Environmental Protection Agency

A PROGRAM TO PROTECT CHILDREN'S HEALTH

School buses carry 25 million of our nation's children each year and they are the safest way to get children to school. Unfortunately, many school buses, especially older ones, emit hazardous gases and particles. CLEAN SCHOOL BUS USA is a program to help communities protect children's health by reducing pollution from diesel school buses.

NEW TECHNOLOGIES MAKE BUS EMISSIONS CLEANER

Modern buses are equipped with up-to-date emission control technologies, but even older buses can take advantage of cleaner technologies and fuels. Particulate filters, like the one installed on the Magic School Bus in this book, can reduce pollution from older buses by *90 percent* or more.

In addition to retrofitting existing school bus fleets with modern emission control devices, communities can adopt better idling policies, use cleaner fuels, and replace very old buses. All these practices will help keep the air cleaner and all of us breathing it safer.

GET HELP FROM THE EPA

CLEAN SCHOOL BUS USA is a common-sense approach to a solvable problem. To learn more about this program and find out about assistance to communities, visit: www.epa.gov/cleanschoolbus.

If we've learned one thing in Ms. Frizzle's class, it is to be ready for anything. Ms. Frizzle is full of surprises. Today we are starting a new science unit about air pollution. We've learned about some far-out things with the Friz, but air pollution sounds like something to get choked up about.

AIR POLLUTION: Substances in the air that cause problems for people and nature.

The Magic School Bus®
Gets Cleaned Up

Prepared with the help of the U.S. Environmental Protection Agency

SCHOLASTIC INC.

New York   Toronto   London   Auckland   Sydney
Mexico City   New Delhi   Hong Kong   Buenos Aires

Arnold   Ralphie   Keesha   Phoebe   Carlos   Tim   Wanda   Dorothy Ann

Written by Kristin Earhart
Illustrated by Carolyn Bracken

Based on *The Magic School Bus* books
written by Joanna Cole and illustrated by Bruce Degen

No part of this publication may be reproduced in whole or in part, stored in a retrieval system,
or transmitted in any form or by any means, electronic, mechanical, photocopying, recording, or
otherwise, without written permission of the publisher. For information regarding permission, write to
Scholastic Inc., Attention: Permissions Department, 557 Broadway, New York, NY 10012.

ISBN-13: 978-0-545-00032-1
ISBN-10: 0-545-00032-7
EPA 420-K-07-01

Copyright © 2007 Joanna Cole and Bruce Degen. Published by Scholastic Inc.
All rights reserved. SCHOLASTIC, THE MAGIC SCHOOL BUS,
and associated logos are trademarks and/or registered trademarks of Scholastic Inc.

12 11 10 9 8 7 6 5 4 3 2   8/0 9/0 10/0 11/0

Designed by Rick DeMonico

First printing, May 2007   Printed in the U.S.A.

"It's that time again!" Ms. Frizzle announces. When we see the sparkle in her eyes, we all know we're in for a class trip.

"We never go on normal field trips," Arnold groans.

"Yeah, but now we're just studying the air," Tim says.

"What could be more normal than that?" Wanda agrees.

We were just leaving the school when Ms. Frizzle gasped.

"I forgot my map!" our teacher exclaimed. "I'll go get it. Stay on the bus, kids."

But when Ms. Frizzle left, our bus started to shake.

With each cough, the bus got smaller. We got as small as a dust particle and we saw lots of stuff in the air.

"Yuck! What is that?" Wanda asked.

"That's particulate matter from the buses," Dorothy Ann said. "It's usually way too small for us to see."

"But it pollutes the air and makes it dirty," Tim said.

THE POLLUTION BITS ARE SO SMALL, THEY CAN GO PLACES THEY SHOULDN'T.

LIKE IN OUR LUNGS!

WHAT IS PARTICULATE MATTER?
by Tim

Most school buses use a kind of fuel called diesel. Diesel exhaust contains billions of bits of soot called particulate matter. These bits of soot can be so small that thousands could fit on the dot at the end of this sentence.

Because the bits are so small, the wind can carry them for many miles.

"Oh, no!" Phoebe called, pointing out the front window.
The wind blew us straight at Mr. Rivera, the crossing guard.

A strong gust of wind blew us right inside Mr. Rivera's nose.

Mr. Rivera didn't know we were inside him!
"The nose hairs help filter out big particles from the air, so they don't go into your lungs," D.A. tells us.
The bus was so tiny it slipped right through the hairs. We were headed down the windpipe.

Once we were in the lungs, we could see that Mr. Rivera had breathed in stuff other than air.

"Smaller particles can go even deeper into the lungs," D.A. told us.

The lungs started to exhale and we began to go faster than ever. A high-pitched sound rang through the bus.

"It's a whistle!" Wanda yelled over the noise.

Mr. Rivera had blown his whistle, and we were shooting straight out into the air.

The wind caught our bus and blew it into the sky.

Our bus was still sputtering and wheezing. We went higher and higher with each cough.

"Look!" Tim called. "There's Ms. Frizzle. She's getting on a bus with Ms. Berk's class."

Then the wind blew us right past the Friz's window in Ms. Berk's bus. She was busy examining her map. She didn't seem to see us. But when she shook her keys, something funny happened to the bus.

The wind blew us to the front of Ms. Berk's bus.
"Where are we going?" Keesha asked.
"According to my research," D.A. said as she looked in her book, "we're moving with the air into the engine of Ms. Berk's school bus."

"We're taking a trip through the bus's engine," D.A. told us. "Right now, we're in the engine block," she said and pointed to a picture in her book. "To get out, we need to follow the exhaust to the tailpipe."

"Look at us!" cried Wanda.

We were covered with bits of soot.

"We've left the engine block. Now we're in the exhaust system," D.A. explained. "Pollution and soot can be left after the fuel burns. We're all covered in particulate matter."

Exhaust was everywhere! It was extremely dirty.

"How will we find Ms. Frizzle?" Phoebe asked.
Then we noticed that the exhaust was going into a special device. And we were going with it!
D.A. looked in her book. "My research shows that this filter traps almost all the particulate matter."

PARTICULATE MATTER FILTER

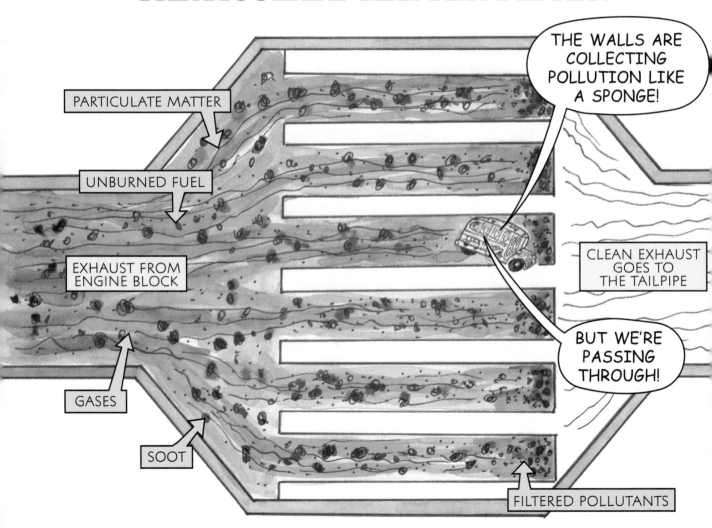

After we went through the filter, we were all clean again!

Then we heard a familiar voice. It was Ms. Frizzle.

"It's wonderful that you already had a filter put on your bus, Ms. Berk. I'm looking forward to having one put on my bus as well," the Friz said.

WE'RE CLEAN!

MY MOM'S NEVER GOING TO BELIEVE THIS!

CLEAN AS A WHISTLE!
by Phoebe

Old diesel buses can make dirty exhaust. Many of them don't have good filters.

Now new filters can be installed in old buses to reduce up to 90 percent of the particulate matter in their exhaust.

WITH THE FILTER, BUS EXHAUST IS MUCH LESS HARMFUL!

Suddenly, we were in an auto shop and we had on mechanics' outfits. Ms. Frizzle was there with a mechanic.

"Class, this is Mr. Spencer," said Ms. Frizzle. "He's going to put a filter on our bus that will clean the exhaust so the bus won't be sick anymore."

We all nodded. After our trip through the engine, we all knew how important Mr. Spencer's work was.

THE FILTER IS GREAT, BUT THERE ARE OTHER WAYS TO REDUCE BUS POLLUTION.

THE CLEAN AIR CHECKLIST

1. Ask your bus driver to turn off the engine when the bus is parked.
2. Keep up with bus maintenance.
3. Use cleaner fuels, like clean diesel fuel or biodiesel.
4. Line buses up side by side, not front to back at school.
5. Get old buses fitted with exhaust cleaning devices like filters and catalysts.
6. Replace really old diesel buses with new clean diesel or compressed natural gas buses.

We helped Mr. Spencer install the particulate filter. Then we got ready to head back to school.

Vroom, vroom. The bus purred to life. We were glad the bus was healthy again.

THERE'S NO MORE SMOKE!

THE BUS IS BETTER THAN EVER!

OTHER BUSES CAN GET BETTER, TOO.

BUT OUR BUS WILL ALWAYS BE THE WEIRDEST BUS!

GOOD NEWS: STARTING IN 2007, ALL NEW DIESEL SCHOOL BUSES WILL HAVE BUILT-IN PARTICULATE MATTER FILTERS WITH MORE IMPROVEMENTS COMING IN 2010.

A PHONE CALL TO SPENCER'S

Telephone: Ring! Ring!

Mr. Spencer: Spencer's! The bus mechanic you can trust!

Caller: Hello, Mr. Spencer? I'm not so sure people *should* trust you!

Mr. Spencer: That's ridiculous!

Caller: But you're in this book that says buses can shrink and fly...

Mr. Spencer: Okay, but...

Caller: And what about saying that kids can pass through a bus filter?

Mr. Spencer: We all know that can't really happen, but...

Caller: And I heard that you wear a wig!

Mr. Spencer: Now wait just a minute! My hair is all-natural!

Caller: It is? And what about the information in this book?

Mr. Spencer: That's all for real, too. Well, except for the shrinking and flying buses and kids passing through filters. Besides, this is a book about a MAGIC School Bus.

Caller: Huh. I guess you're trustworthy after all.

Mr. Spencer: You betcha!